Shape Poems

Compiled by John Foster

KU-338-060

Contents

Acknowledgements

The Editor and Publisher wish to thank the following who have kindly given permission for the use of copyright material:

Pie Corbett for 'A circle is' © 1994 Pie Corbett; John Foster for 'A cube' and 'Moons' both © 1994 John Foster; Ian Larmont for 'All shapes of food' © 1994 Ian Larmont; Tony Mitton for 'Triangles' © 1994 Tony Mitton; Judith Nicholls for 'Square, so there!' © 1994 Judith Nicholls; Celia Warren for 'Find me a shape' © 1994 Celia Warren.

All shapes of food

A triangle of cheese
I spread like paste.
MUNCH MUNCH MUNCH.
Mmmm, what a taste.

A big chocolate biscuit,
A circle, flat and round.
MUNCH MUNCH MUNCH.
Ssh! Don't make a sound.

3

Now, I eat a slice of bread.
This slice is a square.
MUNCH MUNCH MUNCH.
Now, it's not there.

Sandwiches and cakes and buns,
All for me.
How many other shapes
Do I eat for my tea?

Ian Larmont

A circle is

A round hoop.
A bowl of soup.

The sun in the sky.
An apple pie.

A cotton reel.
A bicycle wheel.

Pie Corbett

7

Find me a shape

Find me a triangle . . .

Ears of the cat
As it sits on my lap.
Lick it, stick it,
An envelope flap.

Find me a circle . . .

Coins in my pocket,
A penny or a pound.
Tiddlywinks jumping.
A button on the ground.

Find me a hexagon . . .

Holes in the hive
A honey-bee built.
Patterns on a football
And a patchwork quilt.

Celia Warren

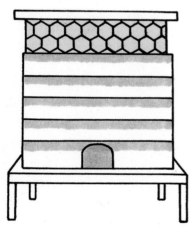

Square, so there!

How many sides has
a big, blue square?
Just four!
How many sides has
a small, red square?
Still four!

How many sides has
ANY kind of square?
ALWAYS four, so there!

Judith Nicholls

Triangles

There's a triangle I sit on.
It's a triangle I like.
It's there in the middle
of my new, red bike.

There are triangles of paper.
They're green and red and white.
The wind blows them across the sky,
when I fly my kite.

But the best kind of triangles
are the ones I eat,
triangles of chocolate,
my favourite sweet.

Tony Mitton

A cube

A cube is solid,
With six sides like a dice.
It can be sweet
like a lump of sugar,
or cold like a block of ice.

John Foster

Moons

The new moon is curved,
like a banana in the sky.

The old moon is round,
like a football kicked up high.

John Foster

16